SAY AAH!

WITHDRAWN

an imprint of Hodder Children's Books

With thanks to Dr Sue Green.

New Experiences

Are We There Yet? My First Holiday
Can I Feed It? My First Pet
I Want That Room! Moving House
I'm Still Important! A New Baby
Open Wide! My First Trip to the Dentist
Say Aah! My First Visit to the Doctor
Where's My Peg? My First Day at School
Where's My Present? My First Party

Published in Great Britain in 2000 by Hodder Wayland,
an imprint of Hodder Children's Books
© Copyright 2000 Hodder Wayland

Editor: Jason Hook
Designer: Tessa Barwick

A Catalogue record for this book is available from the British Library.

ISBN 0 7502 2615 3

Printed and bound in Italy by G. Canale & C.Sp.A., Turin

Hodder Children's Books
A division of Hodder Headline Limited
338 Euston Road, London NW1 3BH

SAY AAH!

My first visit to the doctor

Written by Jen Green

Illustrated by Mike Gordon

HODDER
Wayland

an imprint of Hodder Children's Books

Today I woke up feeling funny.
Mum said I was very hot.

4

Dad phoned and booked a time for me to see the doctor.

My tongue felt furry.

My throat felt like it was on fire.

My ears ached.

I felt like a drum was beating in my head.

What if I came out in spots?

7

Would the doctor give me an injection? Or really big pills? Or horrible medicine?

8

'Don't worry,' said my sister Hannah. 'The doctor will make you better.'

Don't worry!

Mum took me to the doctor's surgery. She gave my name to Mrs Ryan the receptionist.

'Sit down,' said Mrs Ryan.
'The doctor won't be long.'

The waiting room was very busy.
I sat next to a man who kept sneezing.

Then Mrs Ryan called my name.
It was my turn to go in.

'Hello, Edward,' said Dr Ahmed.
'How are you feeling?'

I said my throat was sore and my ears ached. 'Let's take a look,' she said.

The doctor
shone a light in
my throat ...

then in my ears.

16

She felt my neck.

That tickles!

She listened to
my chest with a tool
called a stethoscope.
It was very cold!

17

'Nothing to worry about,' said Dr Ahmed. 'Some medicine will make your throat feel better.'

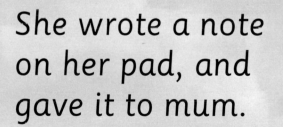

She wrote a note
on her pad, and
gave it to mum.

Outside, we bumped
into Dad and Hannah!
Hannah was limping.

21

We all went back to the doctor.
'What happened to you, Hannah?'
said Dr Ahmed.

'Can you wiggle your toes?'

'See if you can stand on it.'

Ouch! Ouch! Ouch!

23

The doctor said Hannah's ankle was sprained, but not broken. A nurse put a big bandage on it.

Then she gave us each a sticker
for being brave.

On the way home we stopped
at the chemist.

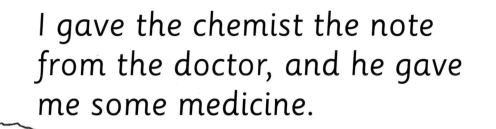

I gave the chemist the note from the doctor, and he gave me some medicine.

At home, Mum gave me my medicine. It tasted fruity. I was feeling better already.

Notes for parents and teachers

This book introduces children to the subjects of illness and going to the doctor. Parents or teachers who read the book with children may find it useful to stop and discuss issues as they come up.

Most children visit the doctor from an early age, for inoculations. However, these early experiences are soon forgotten, so a later trip may seem like a first experience.

All children fall ill occasionally. Sometimes there's no doubt a child is ill, but at other times it's harder to tell. Watch for definite signs of illness, such as vomiting, high temperature, cough or runny nose. If you are seriously worried, contact your family doctor at any time.

Some children feel apprehensive about visiting the doctor. A doctor's surgery may seem a strange, even frightening, place, and the experience of being ill may also be worrying. Encourage the child to talk about his or her feelings. Stress the positive aspects of visiting the doctor, who will find out what is wrong, and may then prescribe something to make the child feel better.

What experiences do the children have of illness? Childhood illnesses include measles, mumps and chicken-pox as well as coughs, colds, sore throats and ear infections. Have the children visited the doctor recently? If so, how did their own experiences differ from the ones described in the book? Common experiences might include inoculations and regular check-ups.

Encourage children to tell the story of their own visit to the doctor, using the book as a framework. The stories could be put together to make a class or group book.

A visit to the doctor may introduce new words, including: temperature, appointment, surgery, waiting room, GP (general practitioner), inoculation, vaccination, injection, infection, prescription. Explain what these words mean.

Use this book for teaching literacy

This book can help you in the literacy hour in the following ways:

- ✓ Children can write simple stories linked to personal experience using the language of the text in this book as a model for their own writing. (Year 1, Term 3: Non-fiction writing composition.)

- ✓ Children can look through the book and try to locate verbs with past and present tense endings. (Year 1, Term 3: Word recognition, graphic knowledge and spelling.)

- ✓ Use of speech bubbles shows a different way of presenting text. (Year 2, Term 2: Sentence construction and punctuation.)

Books to read

Going to the Doctor by Anne Civardi and Stephen Cartright (Usborne Publishing, 1988).
Jenny has a sore throat. Her brother Jack has hurt his arm, while baby Joey is due for his inoculations. Their mum takes her whole family to see Doctor Woody.

Freddie Visits the Doctor by Nicola Smee (Orchard Books, 1997).
Freddie and his bear both have a sore throat. The doctor examines them. The bear turns out to be fine, but Freddie needs some medicine to make him better.

Going to the Doctor by Camilla Jessel (Methuen Children's Books, 1981). When Clare develops a sore throat, her mum takes her down to the doctor's surgery. At first, Clare doesn't want to help the doctor, but in the end he wins her round.

Going to the Doctor by Kate Petty (Franklin Watts, 1987). Sam goes to the doctor for a routine check-up. The book explains what happens during his examination.